BLOCKBUSTERS QUIZ BOOK 3

This book adaptation of *Blockbusters*, the very successful Central television series game, can be used in one of two ways. By yourself you can solve the clues as you would a crossword puzzle, writing the answers in the spaces provided and shading or colouring in the hexagons; or, you can play it as a game with friends, one being the quizmaster and two being competitors, one trying to get a linking pattern of hexagons across and one down.

Whether you solve the clues yourself, or with friends, you'll have hours of amusement and have masses of information at your fingertips.

Blockbusters Quiz Book 3

Based on the Central Independent Television series produced in association with Mark Goodson and Talbot Television Ltd

SPHERE BOOKS LIMITED

First published in Great Britain by
Sphere Books Ltd 1986
27 Wrights Lane, London W8 5TZ
Reprinted 1986
Copyright © 1986 by Sphere Books Ltd
Central logo copyright © 1982
Central Independent Television plc.
Central Television programmes © 1983, 1984, 1985, 1986
Central Independent Television plc.
Reprinted 1987

Questions for *Blockbusters Quiz Book 3* compiled by
Bill Garnett

Sphere Books claim full responsibility for the questions
and answers in this volume and every effort has been made to
ensure their accuracy.

Set in Times

Printed and bound in Great Britain by
Cox & Wyman Ltd, Reading

Blockbusters
Quiz Book 3

M _____	L _____
O _____	S _____
K _____	T _____
D _____	R _____
J _____	C _____
P _____	E _____
H _____	A _____
W _____	V _____
F _____	G _____
B _____	N _____

M: What 'M' is the only primate to get lice?

O: What 'O' killed his father and married his mother?

K: What 'K' is meat cooked on a skewer?

D: What 'D' is a dog named after a Yugoslav province?

J: What 'J' is an Asian monarchy consisting of four main islands?

P: What 'P' rode nine Derby winners?

H: What 'H' is a bumpkin?

W: What 'W' is an Australian marsupial living wild in Yorkshire?

F: What 'F' founded psychoanalysis?

B: What 'B' is the capital of Barbados?

L: What 'L' is a team game borrowed from the Red Indians?

S: What 'S' is a bird belonging to the Queen?

T: What 'T' is a much-married actress?

R: What 'R' is a burrowing mammal – and aimless chatter?

C: What 'C' is a mound of stones forming a memorial or landmark?

E: What 'E' is full of keen desire?

A: What 'A' is a colourless mixture of argon, nitrogen and oxygen?

V: What 'V' was the volcano that wiped out Pompeii?

G: What 'G' was the first man in space?

N: What 'N' is a poisonous alkaloid used as an insecticide?

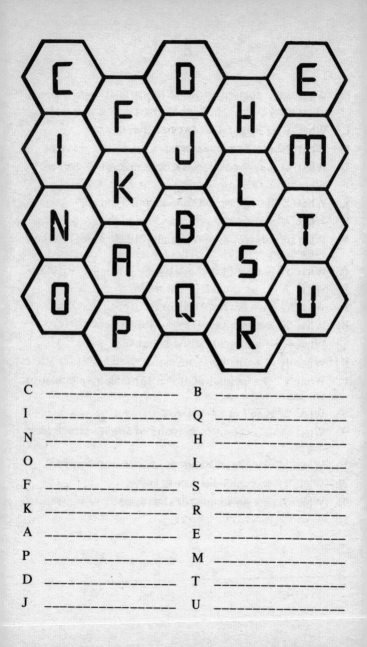

C _____ B _____

I _____ Q _____

N _____ H _____

O _____ L _____

F _____ S _____

K _____ R _____

A _____ E _____

P _____ M _____

D _____ T _____

J _____ U _____

C: What 'C' is a pigtail, a leather-tipped stick – and a signal to an actor?

I: What 'I' was a great Norwegian playwright?

N: What 'N' runs army canteens?

O: What 'O' was the first black hero in English drama?

F: What 'F' is the longest bone in the human body?

K: What 'K' lies between Thailand and Vietnam?

A: What 'A' is the most common metal in the Earth's crust?

P: What 'P' was world motor-racing champion in 1981 and 1983?

D: What 'D' is the oldest continuously inhabited city in the world?

J: What 'J' is an Islamic Holy War?

B: What 'B' is a large monkey with a dog-like muzzle?

Q: What 'Q' comes before sand, silver and step?

H: What 'H' is a quick way of saying SOS?

L: What 'L' was a British soldier who led the Arabs against the Turks?

S: What 'S' is 300 times as sweet as sugar?

R: What 'R' is a marked, greyish-brown American mammal?

E: What 'E' means freedom from pain or trouble?

M: What 'M' is a port-like drink, and a river in Brazil?

T: What 'T' was also known as Lord Greystoke?

U: What 'U' is a flying saucer?

G _____
Y _____
A _____
T _____
V _____
S _____
U _____
B _____
E _____
N _____

I _____
L _____
P _____
O _____
H _____
F _____
D _____
M _____
J _____
R _____

G: What 'G' is a poisonous lizard?

Y: What 'Y' is a horse more than one and less than two years old?

A: What 'A' is the world's longest land mass?

T: What 'T' is a type of roofer and ruler of Britain?

V: What 'V' like a mole likes a hole?

S: What 'S' is the great North African desert?

U: What 'U' is portable weather protection?

B: What 'B' is a nocturnal, carnivorous, burrowing quadruped related to the weasel?

E: What 'E' comes before nut, works and worm?

N: What 'N' was an Englishman grown rich in India?

I: What 'I' is another form of water?

L: What 'L' designed the lions in Trafalgar Square?

P: What 'P' was the earliest known paper?

O: What 'O' is a large, round ball produced by a wasp?

H: What 'H' is a beautiful woman of the Moslem paradise?

F: What 'F' is American for a water tap?

D: What 'D' was a World War II concentration camp?

M: What 'M' is a large South American parrot?

J: What 'J' is a town in India and riding britches?

R: What 'R' is the use of electro-magnetic waves to carry sound?

C _____
E _____
I _____
N _____
R _____
W _____
D _____
K _____
B _____
V _____

F _____
F T _____
T S _____
S Y _____
Y L _____
L G _____
G P _____
P U _____
U J _____
J A _____
A

4

C: What 'C' is a system of religious worship?

E: What 'E' won the Nobel Prize for his work in quantum theory?

I: What 'I' was an English composer of chamber music?

N: What 'N' is a downy surface, a recommendation – and a short sleep?

R: What 'R' is an ordained Jewish official?

W: What 'W' is the people of the southern province of Belgium?

D: What 'D' is another name for crane-fly?

K: What 'K' is a German word meaning broken?

B: What 'B' is a Somerset town noted for its hot springs?

V: What 'V' is a Cross, a London station and was a Queen?

F: What 'F' invented the mercury thermometer?

T: What 'T' is a bear named after a US president?

S: What 'S' is a general term for tailed amphibians?

Y: What 'Y' is to be filled with longing?

L: What 'L' is a primitive, eel-like fish with a round sucking mouth?

G: What 'G' is a public opinion survey?

P: What 'P' is another name for leopard?

U: What 'U' means deep blue?

J: What 'J' is a shabby place, a connecting point between bones – and a cannabis cigarette?

A: What 'A' is a purple or violet kind of quartz?

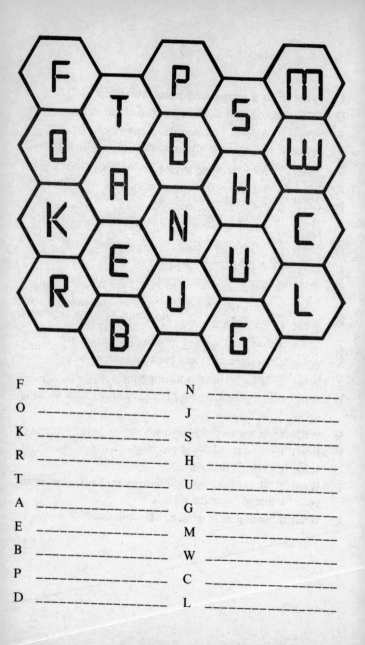

F _____   N _____

O _____   J _____

K _____   S _____

R _____   H _____

T _____   U _____

A _____   G _____

E _____   M _____

B _____   W _____

P _____   C _____

D _____   L _____

F: What 'F' is a young female racehorse?

O: What 'O' is Britain's most honoured actor?

K: What 'K' used to box people in circuses?

R: What 'R' is a group of people of common stock?

T: What 'T' does the song say 'it's a long way to'?

A: What 'A' is the largest living snake?

E: What 'E' executed her sister Mary?

B: What 'B' was the Greek god of wine and merriment?

P: What 'P' means godless?

D: What 'D' is a Spanish surrealist painter?

N: What 'N' was a 19th century hospital reformer?

J: What 'J' supports a floor or ceiling?

S: What 'S' is a herb of the mint family – and a very wise man?

H: What 'H' is a large number, consecrated bread and someone who entertains you?

U: What 'U' is possibly the most fertile country in Africa?

G: What 'G' is a crocodile with a long, extremely narrow snout?

M: What 'M' is the oldest European colony in the Far East?

W: What 'W' is the simplest compound of hydrogen and oxygen?

C: What 'C' is a family of flowering plants that thrives in desert regions?

L: What 'L' comes before bird, like and ship?

M _____   L _____

O _____   S _____

K _____   T _____

D _____   R _____

J _____   C _____

P _____   E _____

H _____   A _____

W _____   V _____

F _____   G _____

B _____   N _____

M: What 'M' is the largest single river in North America?

O: What 'O' formulated a fundamental law of electric current?

K: What 'K' is a falcon that hovers for ground prey?

D: What 'D' was an early photographic process?

J: What 'J' was the Irish author of *Ulysses*?

P: What 'P' is god of the dead, a cartoon dog and a planet?

H: What 'H' was an 18th century furniture maker?

W: What 'W' were strings of shells used by Red Indians as money?

F: What 'F' are vertical rows on a chess board?

B: What 'B' is worthless, deficient, of poor quality?

L: What 'L' was a defensive circle of wagons?

S: What 'S' is now called 'Ho Chi Minh City'?

T: What 'T' was a 'travelling temple' in the Old Testament?

R: What 'R' is the capital of Morocco?

C: What 'C' is a metallic element chemically similar to zinc and mercury?

E: What 'E' preferred a woman to the throne of England?

A: What 'A' is a one-celled animal that moves by changing shape?

V: What 'V' is the Haitian form of witchcraft?

G: What 'G' are tropical lizards that can walk across ceilings upside down?

N: What 'N' was probably the prototype of the unicorn?

C _____   B _____

I _____   Q _____

N _____   H _____

O _____   L _____

F _____   S _____

K _____   R _____

A _____   E _____

P _____   M _____

D _____   T _____

J _____   U _____

C: What 'C' is a unit of quantity of heat?

I: What 'I' was the first Tsar of Russia?

N: What 'N' are tailed amphibians of the salamander family?

O: What 'O' is a loose fibre got by picking old rope to pieces?

F: What 'F' comes before value, cloth and lift?

K: What 'K' is the cat-sized South American 'honey bear'?

A: What 'A' is capital of the Netherlands?

P: What 'P' is a type of barley, something precious – and an infamous harbour?

D: What 'D' was a French mathematician and philosopher?

J: What 'J' is a small, rugged, multi-purpose vehicle?

B: What 'B' founded the Boy Scouts in 1908?

Q: What 'Q' is a pigtail?

H: What 'H' do you make while the sun shines?

L: What 'L' means chemically unstable?

S: What 'S' is both a sea and a fresh water fish?

R: What 'R' is a market town – and an archbishop?

E: What 'E' is supposedly home to the Yeti?

M: What 'M' makes offers you can't refuse?

T: What 'T' is the world's most densely populated country?

U: What 'U' was the Roman name for Odysseus?

G _ _ _ _ _ _ _ _ _ _ _ _ _ _ _   I _ _ _ _ _ _ _ _ _ _ _ _ _ _ _

Y _ _ _ _ _ _ _ _ _ _ _ _ _ _ _   L _ _ _ _ _ _ _ _ _ _ _ _ _ _ _

A _ _ _ _ _ _ _ _ _ _ _ _ _ _ _   P _ _ _ _ _ _ _ _ _ _ _ _ _ _ _

T _ _ _ _ _ _ _ _ _ _ _ _ _ _ _   O _ _ _ _ _ _ _ _ _ _ _ _ _ _ _

V _ _ _ _ _ _ _ _ _ _ _ _ _ _ _   H _ _ _ _ _ _ _ _ _ _ _ _ _ _ _

S _ _ _ _ _ _ _ _ _ _ _ _ _ _ _   F _ _ _ _ _ _ _ _ _ _ _ _ _ _ _

U _ _ _ _ _ _ _ _ _ _ _ _ _ _ _   D _ _ _ _ _ _ _ _ _ _ _ _ _ _ _

B _ _ _ _ _ _ _ _ _ _ _ _ _ _ _   M _ _ _ _ _ _ _ _ _ _ _ _ _ _ _

E _ _ _ _ _ _ _ _ _ _ _ _ _ _ _   J _ _ _ _ _ _ _ _ _ _ _ _ _ _ _

N _ _ _ _ _ _ _ _ _ _ _ _ _ _ _   R _ _ _ _ _ _ _ _ _ _ _ _ _ _ _

G: What 'G' is an adult male goose?

Y: What 'Y' comes after back, ship and builders?

A: What 'A' are the essential organic acids which link to form protein in living tissue?

T: What 'T' is the capital of Taiwan?

V: What 'V' creeps by night and sucks blood?

S: What 'S' is sodium chloride?

U: What 'U' was a Norwegian Nobel Prize-winning novelist?

B: What 'B' are there more kinds of than any other animal?

E: What 'E' lies between Columbia and Peru?

N: What 'N' are fragments of crushed cocoa-beans – and pen-points?

I: What 'I' was a sacred bird to the ancient Egyptians?

L: What 'L' is the *de facto* capital of Bolivia?

P: What 'P' is the setting agent in jam?

O: What 'O' is a kind of negro sorcery?

H: What 'H' built Britain's longest wall?

F: What 'F' is arable land left unseeded for a year?

D: What 'D' is a tap, an adept at games – and a flat fish?

M: What 'M' is the highest capital in Europe?

J: What 'J' was called 'the wisest fool in Christendom'?

R: What 'R' is someone with extreme hydrophobia?

C _____
E _____
I _____
N _____
R _____
W _____
D _____
K _____
B _____
V _____

F _____
T _____
S _____
Y _____
L _____
G _____
P _____
U _____
J _____
A _____

C: What 'C' is the world's second largest country?

E: What 'E' is the process whereby a solid or liquid is resolved into vapour?

I: What 'I' are the most numerous creatures on Earth?

N: What 'N' means bond or connection?

R: What 'R' is the capital of Burma?

W: What 'W' is a rotary internal combustion engine?

D: What 'D' is the American word for maisonette?

K: What 'K' is sharp, eager – and a wail?

B: What 'B' composed the Brandenburg Concertos and the B Minor Mass?

V: What 'V' is a unit of electromotive force?

F: What 'F' is a predatory bird related to the eagle?

T: What 'T' won the Wimbledon mixed doubles with John Lloyd in 1983 and 1984?

S: What 'S' is a sort of flattened sea urchin?

Y: What 'Y' comes before club, full and hostel?

L: What 'L' is the protective substance secreted by an insect of the same name?

G: What 'G' is a small room just under the roof of a house?

P: What 'P' supposedly drove all snakes out of Ireland?

U: What 'U' is an open sore?

J: What 'J' is slang for both a chamber pot and German soldier?

A: What 'A' is a Portuguese-speaking republic in West-central Africa?

F _____

O _____

K _____

R _____

T _____

A _____

E _____

B _____

P _____

D _____

N _____

J _____

S _____

H _____

U _____

G _____

M _____

W _____

C _____

L _____

F: What 'F' is literally 'a man of all work'?

O: What 'O' means to obscure or make bewildering?

K: What 'K' is a cotton wool used for stuffing cushions?

R: What 'R' is a root with a peppery taste?

T: What 'T' is something forbidden?

A: What 'A' is a substance our bodies produce to fight invading viruses?

E: What 'E' is equidistant from the North and South Poles?

B: What 'B' is an English philosopher – and a cured cut of pig?

P: What 'P' are marine worms that mate without meeting?

D: What 'D' is the lower section of a room's wall when faced with wood?

N: What 'N' is a stingy person?

J: What 'J' comes before leg, black and set?

S: What 'S' is an outward sign of inward grace?

H: What 'H' is the Eve of All Saints' Day?

U: What 'U' is the smallest South American republic?

G: What 'G' is another word for bushbaby?

M: What 'M' wrote about political machinations in *The Prince*?

W: What 'W' is pale or exhausted-looking?

C: What 'C' is India's largest city?

L: What 'L' is our most popular beetle?

M _____   L _____

O _____   S _____

K _____   T _____

D _____   R _____

J _____   C _____

P _____   E _____

H _____   A _____

W _____   V _____

F _____   G _____

B _____   N _____

M: What 'M' was an 18th century English dandy who affected European ways?

O: What 'O' is a South American cat?

K: What 'K' is a small barrel?

D: What 'D' is colour-blindness?

J: What 'J' is the Old Testament God?

P: What 'P' is a great Brazilian footballer?

H: What 'H' is an old-fashioned word meaning 'as a result'?

W: What 'W' comes before coat, line or band?

F: What 'F' comes before lights, land and rings?

B: What 'B' is connected cells, hammered brass – and a military gun emplacement?

L: What 'L' is part of Newfoundland and a gun dog?

S: What 'S' conquered Jerusalem in 1187?

T: What 'T' was a doubting disciple?

R: What 'R' stands for radio detection and ranging?

C: What 'C' is the collective name for the mountains of North and Central Wales?

E: What 'E' selects prizewinning premium bonds?

A: What 'A' is the capital of South Yemen?

V: What 'V' was a third century Christian martyr?

G: What 'G' comes before plank, show and way?

N: What 'N' is a pop-eyed toad with a muttering croak?

C _____
I _____
N _____
O _____
F _____
K _____
A _____
P _____
D _____
J _____

B _____
Q _____
H _____
L _____
S _____
R _____
E _____
M _____
T _____
U _____

C: What 'C' means to remove an animal from a flock?

I: What 'I' was an epic poem on the siege of Troy?

N: What 'N' is Africa's longest river?

O: What 'O' is a Japanese woman's sash?

F: What 'F' is a member of a mendicant order of the Catholic church?

K: What 'K' is the sum of a person's actions that determines his destiny?

A: What 'A' is man's nearest living relative?

P: What 'P' comes before stripe, point and up?

D: What 'D' is a retaining barrier – and an animal's mother?

J: What 'J' is a small, usually solitary, wild dog?

B: What 'B' means to worry or nag – and lives in a set?

Q: What 'Q' is a medical charlatan?

H: What 'H' was the painter who wrote *Mein Kampf*?

L: What 'L' was once capital of Russia?

S: What 'S' was a 12th–19th century Japanese warrior?

R: What 'R' is the condensation of water vapour in the air?

E: What 'E' was a classical English composer?

M: What 'M' is one of the most important food fishes?

T: What 'T' is the eighth letter of the Greek alphabet?

U: What 'U' is a small, four-stringed guitar?

G _____
Y _____
A _____
T _____
V _____
S _____
U _____
B _____
E _____
N _____

I _____
L _____
P _____
O _____
H _____
F _____
D _____
M _____
J _____
R _____

G: What 'G' is a method of strangulation used as capital punishment in Spain?

Y: What 'Y' is a sharp, shrill cry?

A: What 'A' is a slow movement in music?

T: What 'T' is fibrous tissue joining muscle to bone?

V: What 'V' was a Spanish portrait painter?

S: What 'S' is a seaweed-covered part of the North Atlantic?

U: What 'U' is the world's major economic power?

B: What 'B' means madhouse or scene of uproar?

E: What 'E' founded the Christian Scientists?

N: What 'N' is the capital of Kenya?

I: What 'I' comes before bred, gotten and advised?

L: What 'L' is molten rock?

P: What 'P' is Latin for fishes – and the twelfth sign of the Zodiac?

O: What 'O' means flattened at its poles?

H: What 'H' is the drug from which we get the word assassin?

F: What 'F' is a domesticated form of the Asian polecat?

D: What 'D' was the Greek philosopher who lived in a tub?

M: What 'M' was beheaded by her sister?

J: What 'J' is a hard gemstone, usually green?

R: What 'R' is a European capital with more rainfall than London?

C _____	F _____
E _____	FT _____
I _____	T _____
N _____	S _____
R _____	Y _____
W _____	L _____
D _____	G _____
K _____	P _____
B _____	U _____
V _____	J _____
	A _____

C: What 'C' is the art of writing beautiful scripts by hands?

E: What 'E' commanded the allied forces in Europe from 1943 to 1945?

I: What 'I' is a river – and an Egyptian goddess?

N: What 'N' was an early species of prehistoric man?

R: What 'R' comes before sea, deer and currant?

W: What 'W' is a snooker player nicknamed the Whirlwind?

D: What 'D' is an imaginary line around longitude 180° West?

K: What 'K' is china clay?

B: What 'B' was the French author of more than eighty novels?

V: What 'V' is space devoid of matter?

F: What 'F' is a group of people related by marriage or birth?

T: What 'T' is a dance named after a spider?

S: What 'S' was largely destroyed by an earthquake in 1906?

Y: What 'Y' is Japanese currency – and desire?

L: What 'L', meaning 'freetown', is the capital of Gabon?

G: What 'G' is a pungent plant of the onion family?

P: What 'P' was a 14th century Italian poet?

U: What 'U' is an institute of higher learning?

J: What 'J' is a large South American cat?

A: What 'A' is a composition for use by a choir in church?

F _____

O _____

K _____

R _____

T _____

A _____

E _____

B _____

P _____

D _____

N _____

J _____

S _____

H _____

U _____

G _____

M _____

W _____

C _____

L _____

F: What 'F' is the southernmost tip of Greenland – and the northernmost of South Island, New Zealand?

O: What 'O' is a woodwind, double reed instrument?

K: What 'K' is a skirt?

R: What 'R' is the US president who gave his first name to a bear?

T: What 'T' is a common East African gazelle?

A: What 'A' is a curved load-bearing structure?

E: What 'E' was a Greek dramatist who wrote some eighty plays?

B: What 'B' is the capital of Thailand?

P: What 'P' was the Spanish painter who co-founded cubism?

D: What 'D' is oozy?

N: What 'N' supposedly fiddled while Rome burned?

J: What 'J' is a target in bowls, a lifting mechanism – and a playing card?

S: What 'S' are snipe-like birds found on seashores worldwide?

H: What 'H' comes before carbon, electric and foil?

U: What 'U' was a mediaeval symbol of virginity?

G: What 'G' is the sacred river of India?

M: What 'M' is a large, deadly snake?

W: What 'W' was a German operatic composer?

C: What 'C' is a blow with the first – or part of a sleeve?

L: What 'L' is an oil rich North African Republic?

M	_____	L	_____
O	_____	S	_____
K	_____	T	_____
D	_____	R	_____
J	_____	C	_____
P	_____	E	_____
H	_____	A	_____
W	_____	V	_____
F	_____	G	_____
B	_____	N	_____

M: What 'M' was the composer who began his career at four?

O: What 'O' is a rectangle with unequal adjacent sides?

K: What 'K' is the capital of Pakistan?

D: What 'D' was the English poet who was Dean of St Paul's?

J: What 'J' makes you yellow?

P: What 'P' is a black or melanistic variety of leopard?

H: What 'H' means a large mass – and was incredible in a TV series?

W: What 'W' comes before proof, vane or forecast?

F: What 'F' lie 200 miles north-west of the Shetlands?

B: What 'B' is a game played on a double board with counters and dice?

L: What 'L' is the capital of Peru?

S: What 'S' is a small fish of the herring family?

T: What 'T' is a sauce made from peppers?

R: What 'R' was Zimbabwe?

C: What 'C' is an underground cell or vault?

E: What 'E' built Paris' most famous landmark?

A: What 'A' is a narrow tube attached to the large intestine and closed at one end?

V: What 'V' was a French science fiction writer?

G: What 'G' is a dark red semi-precious gem?

N: What 'N' are star clusters and gas clouds in space?

C _____   B _____

I _____   Q _____

N _____   H _____

O _____   L _____

F _____   S _____

K _____   R _____

A _____   E _____

P _____   M _____

D _____   T _____

J _____   U _____

C: What 'C' is the cabin of a half-decked boat – and a young coal fish?

I: What 'I' is the Chinese book of divination?

N: What 'N' was Egyptian president from 1956–1970?

O: What 'O' is the back of the head?

F: What 'F' is an agent, or one who acts for another?

K: What 'K' is a South African desert?

A: What 'A' is a calculator made up of beads on wire?

P: What 'P' is a medium-sized bird found worldwide?

D: What 'D' wrote *Crime and Punishment*?

J: What 'J' is South Africa's largest city?

B: What 'B' means to roar like a bull?

Q: What 'Q' is a bitter medicine made from bark?

H: What 'H' is an insect whose name rhymes with a word for ice-cream cone?

L: What 'L' is the capital of Portugal?

S: What 'S' was the literary language of ancient India?

R: What 'R' is the oldest US president?

E: What 'E' is an elongated fish lacking pelvic fins?

M: What 'M' is a supply chamber, a store room for arms – and an illustrated periodical?

T: What 'T' comes before land, mat and tennis?

U: What 'U' is the inner bone of the forearm?

G _____	I _____
Y _____	L _____
A _____	P _____
T _____	O _____
V _____	H _____
S _____	F _____
U _____	D _____
B _____	M _____
E _____	J _____
N _____	R _____

G: What 'G' is an elastic fluid that has neither shape nor volume?

Y: What 'Y' comes before fever, ochre and hammer?

A: What 'A' is an Afrikaans word meaning 'Separate development'?

T: What 'T' is a small freshwater turtle?

V: What 'V' was a great French philosopher and writer?

S: What 'S' is a light, loose-fitting shoe for indoor use?

U: What 'U' is a silvery radio-active element?

B: What 'B' was once called East Pakistan?

E: What 'E' is a song of lamentation, especially for the dead?

N: What 'N' is a type of smooth-skinned peach?

I: What 'I' is one of the most abundant of African antelopes?

L: What 'L' is milk sugar?

P: What 'P' is the succulent fruit of a spiny plant?

O: What 'O' is someone to whom another is legally bound by contract?

H: What 'H' is probably the most abundant element in the universe?

F: What 'F' is a boring chore – and a cigarette?

D: What 'D' is the sea below sea-level?

M: What 'M' builds an incubator to hatch its eggs?

J: What 'J' did Napoleon divorce in 1809?

R: What 'R' is a vast American mountain chain?

C _____	F _____
E _____	T _____
I _____	S _____
N _____	Y _____
R _____	L _____
W _____	G _____
D _____	P _____
K _____	U _____
B _____	J _____
V _____	A _____

C: What 'C' is a small fragment?

E: What 'E' is bordered by Somalia, Kenya and Sudan?

I: What 'I' was International Rugby Champion 1984–5?

N: What 'N' is slang for police informer?

R: What 'R' invented a cube?

W: What 'W' is an ugly African pig?

D: What 'D' means scanty supply of?

K: What 'K' is the capital of the Sudan?

B: What 'B' is played with a ball and bat on a diamond-shaped pitch?

V: What 'V' means to waver or hesitate?

F: What 'F' is a tiny mythical being with magic powers?

T: What 'T' is a small nail, saddlery – and a long, loose stitch?

S: What 'S' was a beetle held sacred by the ancient Egyptians?

Y: What 'Y' is a form of old German spoken by East European Jews?

L: What 'L' is another name for the Crocodile River?

G: What 'G' is the third largest city in Britain?

P: What 'P' is an unpleasant smell?

U: What 'U' is an ochre-like natural pigment?

J: What 'J' wrote the first dictionary?

A: What 'A' is a suspension of liquid in a gas?

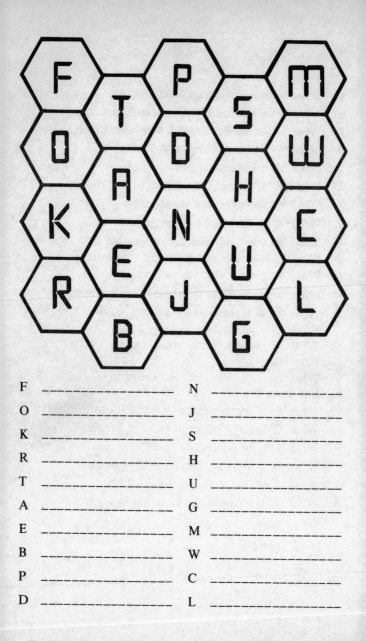

F _____

O _____

K _____

R _____

T _____

A _____

E _____

B _____

P _____

D _____

N _____

J _____

S _____

H _____

U _____

G _____

M _____

W _____

C _____

L _____

F: What 'F' is a Turkish cap – and a sacred city in Morocco?

O: What 'O' comes before well, skin and paint?

K: What 'K' is a racist US secret society?

R: What 'R' is the capital of Iceland?

T: What 'T' is a crisp, plain, glossy fabric?

A: What 'A' is the tree called 'guardian of riverbanks'?

E: What 'E' is the world's largest pachyderm?

B: What 'B' is the Devil?

P: What 'P' is a vertical supporting structure?

D: What 'D' is Europe's second longest river?

N: What 'N' was India's first Prime Minister?

J: What 'J' are the major veins of the neck?

S: What 'S' is the currency of Kenya?

H: What 'H' is farming?

U: What 'U' is the world's largest country?

G: What 'G' won the Grand National in 1982?

M: What 'M' was the sea cow mistaken by Columbus for a mermaid?

W: What 'W' wrote *The Compleat Angler*?

C: What 'C' is a band of singers?

L: What 'L' is a reptile – and England's southernmost point?

M _____
O _____
K _____
D _____
J _____
P _____
H _____
W _____
F _____
B _____

L _____
S _____
T _____
R _____
C _____
E _____
A _____
V _____
G _____
N _____

M: What 'M' lives underground – on worms?

O: What 'O' comes before licence, peak and hand?

K: What 'K' is the capital of Jamaica?

D: What 'D' was the 17th century poet and satirist?

J: What 'J' is obscure and pretentious language?

P: What 'P' is a member of the whale family?

H: What 'H' used elephants to invade Italy?

W: What 'W' does a cricketer bat in front of?

F: What 'F' consists of over 800 islands in the South West Pacific?

B: What 'B' was the archbishop murdered in Canterbury Cathedral?

L: What 'L' is an aquatic blood-sucking worm?

S: What 'S' – as well as spiders – are arachnids?

T: What 'T' is slang for a Welshman?

R: What 'R' was a prolific Dutch painter?

C: What 'C' is the USA's most highly populated state?

E: What 'E' is the female reproductive cell?

A: What 'A' was Queen Victoria's consort?

V: What 'V' are large carrion-eating birds?

G: What 'G' comes before house, paper and ware?

N: What 'N' is the second outermost planet of the solar system?

C _____

I _____

N _____

O _____

F _____

K _____

A _____

P _____

D _____

J _____

B _____

Q _____

H _____

L _____

S _____

R _____

E _____

M _____

T _____

U _____

C: What 'C' was a Roman Emperor notorious for his cruelty?

I: What 'I' is a Moslem priest?

N: What 'N' is a wet Scottish monster?

O: What 'O' is the canal from mouth to gullet?

F: What 'F' are the greatest jumpers for their size in the animal kingdom?

K: What 'K' is a citadel within a Russian city?

A: What 'A' are substances tending to lose a positive ion?

P: What 'P' are the world's most wonderful tombs?

D: What 'D' was the Archbishop of Canterbury who lived through seven reigns?

J: What 'J' is a sudden shake, an unsettling shock – and a container?

B: What 'B' means two-footed?

Q: What 'Q' is the second-largest Australian state?

H: What 'H' is robust – and an English novelist?

L: What 'L' is a pantry?

S: What 'S' are fishes whose males have the babies?

R: What 'R' comes from the Czech and means forced labour?

E: What 'E' is hard black wood?

M: What 'M' is Canada's national emblem?

T: What 'T' are the most primitive social insects?

U: What 'U' comes before violet, marine and sound?

G _____		I _____
Y _____		L _____
A _____		P _____
T _____		O _____
V _____		H _____
S _____		F _____
U _____		D _____
B _____		M _____
E _____		J _____
N _____		R _____

G: What 'G' are longitudes calculated from?

Y: What 'Y' is chatter – and a long-haired mountain ox?

A: What 'A' are flowerless plants living mostly in water?

T: What 'T' is the largest of the cats?

V: What 'V' is a gentleman's gentleman?

S: What 'S' was a French philosopher who won the 1964 Nobel Prize?

U: What 'U' means very many (times)?

B: What 'B' is a liqueur – and a monastic order?

E: What 'E' is the largest of the antelopes?

N: What 'N' was a one-eyed, one-armed British admiral?

I: What 'I' is a mental defective?

L: What 'L' means transparent or clear?

P: What 'P' is the Sovereign Pontiff?

O: What 'O' wrote *The Art of Love*?

H: What 'H' is salted meat, the back of the thigh – and a bad actor?

F: What 'F' is a short fictitious story with a moral at the end?

D: What 'D' comes before light, dream and break?

M: What 'M' is a baboon related to the drill?

J: What 'J' advanced psychoanalysis?

R: What 'R' is where Magna Carta was signed?

C	_____	F _____
E	_____	T _____
I	_____	S _____
N	_____	Y _____
R	_____	L _____
W	_____	G _____
D	_____	P _____
K	_____	U _____
B	_____	J _____
V	_____	A _____

C: What 'C' is called 'the windy city'?

E: What 'E' invented the electric light bulb?

I: What 'I' is the largest American lizard?

N: What 'N' designed Regent's Park and Marble Arch?

R: What 'R' is a flat floating structure – and a film star?

W: What 'W' are Madame Tussaud's models made of?

D: What 'D' is a plant named from the French for lion's tooth?

K: What 'K' is a tail-less, flight-less New Zealand bird?

B: What 'B' is the chief ore of aluminium?

V: What 'V' is drapery round the edge of a bed?

F: What 'F' is the world's leading exporter of pulp and paper?

T: What 'T' is multi-processed soya 'meat'?

S: What 'S' is dismissal, dry white wine – and a bag?

Y: What 'Y' is the abominable snowman?

L: What 'L' is a Hungarian composer – and a rhyming slang for drunk?

G: What 'G' left the Common Market in 1985?

P: What 'P' is inflammation of the tooth sockets?

U: What 'U' is a leading actor's stand-in?

J: What 'J' was formerly Karol Wojtyla of Cracow?

A: What 'A' is a mixture or compound of two or more metals?

Letter		Letter	
F	_____	N	_____
O	_____	J	_____
K	_____	S	_____
R	_____	H	_____
T	_____	U	_____
A	_____	G	_____
E	_____	M	_____
B	_____	W	_____
P	_____	C	_____
D	_____	L	_____

F: What 'F' is a long pointed tooth?

O: What 'O' founded a political party?

K: What 'K' do you stir with to stir up strife?

R: What 'R' was an impressionist French composer?

T: What 'T' is used by surveyors to measure angles?

A: What 'A' is a South American grazing animal related to the llama?

E: What 'E' is a Turkish title of respect?

B: What 'B' is a beak, an obsolete weapon and a note of charges?

P: What 'P' constricts its prey to death?

D: What 'D' wrote *The Three Musketeers*?

N: What 'N' was the last Czar of Russia?

J: What 'J' comes before ass, boot and knife?

S: What 'S' is St Nicholas?

H: What 'H' was the battle which changed the English language?

U: What 'U' means emit as sound?

G: What 'G' lies between Mexico and Honduras?

M: What 'M' is deep crimson?

W: What 'W' are fancifully found on Wimbledon Common?

C: What 'C' is where the Pilgrim fathers first landed in America?

L: What 'L' is an azure mineral used as a gemstone?

M _____   L _____

O _____   S _____

K _____   T _____

D _____   R _____

J _____   C _____

P _____   E _____

H _____   A _____

W _____   V _____

F _____   G _____

B _____   N _____

26

M: What 'M' is a gun, a TV series, and a double-sized bottle?

O: What 'O' founded the Holy Roman Empire?

K: What 'K' is a powder used to darken eyelids?

D: What 'D' was the Anglo-Saxon tax levied to buy off the Danes?

J: What 'J' is a holy city for three religions?

P: What 'P' is a scaly anteater?

H: What 'H' is an old word for stockings – and a watering tube?

W: What 'W' comes before chair, base and wright?

F: What 'F' was the last king of Egypt?

B: What 'B' is a poetic word for a command?

L: What 'L' is a peewit?

S: What 'S' is an oriental flat-bottomed boat?

T: What 'T' is a schedule of rates or prices?

R: What 'R' was a French impressionist painter?

C: What 'C' is a spontaneously composed West Indian song?

E: What 'E' is a pouring forth?

A: What 'A' is a fossilised resin from prehistoric trees?

V: What 'V' was a major World War I battle?

G: What 'G' is a desert-living African rodent – and a British household pet?

N: What 'N' was the Corsican who became Emperor of France?

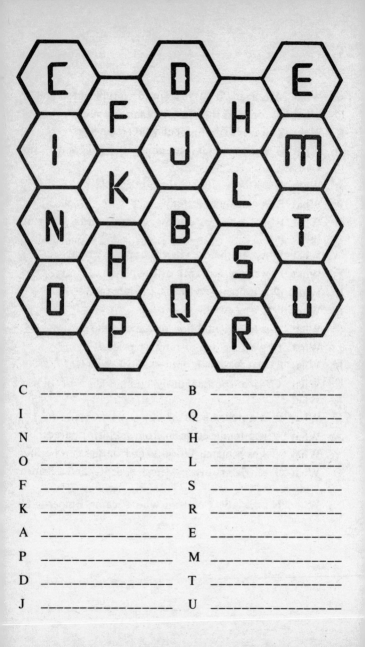

C _____   B _____

I _____   Q _____

N _____   H _____

O _____   L _____

F _____   S _____

K _____   R _____

A _____   E _____

P _____   M _____

D _____   T _____

J _____   U _____

27

C: What 'C' is a fish of the carp family – and a make of lock?

I: What 'I' is a small demon?

N: What 'N' was a US president who resigned?

O: What 'O' was an unknown animal till 1901?

F: What 'F' equals 1.8 metres?

K: What 'K' is the only truly oceanic gull?

A: What 'A' is the capital of Algeria?

P: What 'P' comes before pocket, axe and up?

D: What 'D' was a Greek who feasted with a sword hung over him by a hair?

J: What 'J' is the largest order of the Catholic church?

B: What 'B' produced the first petrol-powered car?

Q: What 'Q' is a four-footed animal?

H: What 'H' is a climbing plant – and an informal dance?

L: What 'L' first flew the Atlantic solo?

S: What 'S' is a small perfumed bag?

R: What 'R' is Germany's industrial district?

E: What 'E' is the US sculptor with work in Hyde Park?

M: What 'M' is molten rock within the Earth's crust?

T: What 'T' is a freshwater member of the salmon family?

U: What 'U' is the objective case of we?

G _____   I _____

Y _____   L _____

A _____   P _____

T _____   O _____

V _____   H _____

S _____   F _____

U _____   D _____

B _____   M _____

E _____   J _____

N _____   R _____

28

G: What 'G' dropped balls from the leaning tower of Pisa?

Y: What 'Y' is a sailing vessel?

A: What 'A' is the fruit of the *Amygdalus Communis*?

T: What 'T' kills some 100,000 Britons each year?

V: What 'V' is the capital of Malta?

S: What 'S' is a shoe hollowed from one piece of wood?

U: What 'U' holds the ashes of the dead?

B: What 'B' are nomadic desert Arabs?

E: What 'E' is the same?

N: What 'N' was the first president of Tanzania?

I: What 'I' is the fourth most abundant substance in the Earth's crust?

L: What 'L' is a small-clawed lobster or crayfish?

P: What 'P' is a toll-bar, a freshwater fish, and a weapon?

O: What 'O' wrote *Animal Farm*?

H: What 'H' is a British film company – and a blunt instrument?

F: What 'F' was five times world champion racing driver?

D: What 'D' grows to thirty metres and can fruit for 300 years?

M: What 'M' is slang for mean?

J: What 'J' is the month named after Caesar?

R: What 'R' had the heart of a lion?

C _____ F _____

E _____ T _____

I _____ S _____

N _____ Y _____

R _____ L _____

W _____ G _____

D _____ P _____

K _____ U _____

B _____ J _____

V _____ A _____

29

C: What 'C' treat feet?

E: What 'E' removed marble sculptures from the Parthenon to the British Museum?

I: What 'I' means to call into question?

N: What 'N' comes before mare, shade and shirt?

R: What 'R' introduced the potato to Britain?

W: What 'W' is a type of willow – and someone in tears?

D: What 'D' were the oldest sons of the kings of France?

K: What 'K' removes waste products from the blood?

B: What 'B' is a spring balance used to gauge water depth?

V: What 'V' was the home of Haydn, Mozart, Beethoven, Schubert, Mahler, Brahms and Freud?

F: What 'F' is a deposit of polluting particles?

T: What 'T' cost up to £10 a pound in 17th century England?

S: What 'S' is the language of East Africa?

Y: What 'Y' is a coarse rough type?

L: What 'L' was the US president slain at a play?

G: What 'G' is a substance in between solid and liquid?

P: What 'P' is a large South American rodent?

U: What 'U' is an implement or tool?

J: What 'J' was the maiden who led an army?

A: What 'A' is the largest, most important artery?

F _____	N _____
O _____	J _____
K _____	S _____
R _____	H _____
T _____	U _____
A _____	G _____
E _____	M _____
B _____	W _____
P _____	C _____
D _____	L _____

30

F: What 'F' discovered electro-magnetic induction?

O: What 'O' is a German town – and a composer?

K: What 'K' comes before calorie, hertz and watt?

R: What 'R' were first used in war by the Chinese in the 13th century?

T: What 'T' winters in the Antarctic and spends the summer in the Arctic?

A: What 'A' is a respiratory disease?

E: What 'E' is the largest Australian bird?

B: What 'B' is a city divided by a wall?

P: What 'P' was a 6th century BC Greek mathematician?

D: What 'D' is to fish by letting bait bob on water?

N: What 'N' is a hookah pipe?

J: What 'J' was US president from 1963 to 1969?

S: What 'S' is the capital of El Salvador?

H: What 'H' was the messenger of the gods?

U: What 'U' is moneylending at exhorbitant interest?

G: What 'G' are the elementary units of heredity?

M: What 'M' is a tropical tree of hard red wood?

W: What 'W' is something that comes every seven days?

C: What 'C' is the roe of sturgeon?

L: What 'L' was the leading protestant of the Reformation?

M _____ L _____

O _____ S _____

K _____ T _____

D _____ R _____

J _____ C _____

P _____ E _____

H _____ A _____

W _____ V _____

F _____ G _____

B _____ N _____

31

M: What 'M' is the highest class of animals?

O: What 'O' is a sultanate in South West Asia?

K: What 'K' is the indentation in the bottom of a glass bottle?

D: What 'D' comes before horse, continent and ages?

J: What 'J' was the American novelist who lived mainly in England?

P: What 'P''s beak can hold more than his belly can?

H: What 'H' means Spanish?

W: What 'W' is the antonym of husband?

F: What 'F' is twelve inches?

B: What 'B' is the world's bestselling book?

L: What 'L' is the sound-producing cavity in the windpipe?

S: What 'S' is Swahili for a journey?

T: What 'T' were cave dwellers?

R: What 'R' was a great Renaissance artist?

C: What 'C' is a wedge used to stop a wheel moving?

E: What 'E' is a newt?

A: What 'A' is a black sticky mixture of minerals containing bitumen?

V: What 'V' is where the Confederates surrendered in the US civil war?

G: What 'G' is a Japanese female entertainer?

N: What 'N' is a tendency to self-worship?

C _____   B _____

I _____   Q _____

N _____   H _____

O _____   L _____

F _____   S _____

K _____   R _____

A _____   E _____

P _____   M _____

D _____   T _____

J _____   U _____

32

C: What 'C' is an often fatal disease endemic in India?

I: What 'I' is senseless?

N: What 'N' was Napoleon's general at Waterloo?

O: What 'O' is the world centre for port (wine)?

F: What 'F' played cricket and soccer for England – and held the world long jump record?

K: What 'K' is a rounded protuberance?

A: What 'A' is someone lacking pigment in their skin and hair?

P: What 'P' is a species of whale that sometimes loses its way?

D: What 'D' means to believe, consider or judge?

J: What 'J' is the river where Jesus was baptised?

B: What 'B' is played on a table with three balls and a rod?

Q: What 'Q' are the hypothetical bases of atomic particles?

H: What 'H' is to push your way, or jostle?

L: What 'L' wrote *Hiawatha*?

S: What 'S' connects the Mediterranean and the Red Sea?

R: What 'R' is a bird with a red breast?

E: What 'E' is either pole of an electric battery?

M: What 'M' is a soft-bodied grub?

T: What 'T' comes before worm, measure and deck?

U: What 'U' is a lifeline?

G _____   I _____

Y _____   L _____

A _____   P _____

T _____   O _____

V _____   H _____

S _____   F _____

U _____   D _____

B _____   M _____

E _____   J _____

N _____   R _____

33

G: What 'G' was an English portrait painter?

Y: What 'Y' means over there?

A: What 'A' comes before cyclone, macassar and climax?

T: What 'T' are pungent aromatic leaves used as flavouring?

V: What 'V' is a farewell speech?

S: What 'S' is the capital of Chile?

U: What 'U' is an undercurrent flowing contrary to a surface current?

B: What 'B' is a cardinal's cap – and a make of gun?

E: What 'E' spontaneously recovers its shape after distortion?

N: What 'N' was destroyed by an atom bomb?

I: What 'I' is an image of Christ in the Eastern church?

L: What 'L' is a long-shaped weapon?

P: What 'P' was a major Russian literary figure?

O: What 'O' is a South African river, a French town and a fruit?

H: What 'H' was the Greek goddess of health?

F: What 'F' is an artificially high voice?

D: What 'D' wrote *The Origin of Species*?

M: What 'M' comes from deers and is used in perfume?

J: What 'J' was the US president who created the Republican party?

R: What 'R' is a type of grass – and a British film star?

C	_____	F	_____
E	_____	T	_____
I	_____	S	_____
N	_____	Y	_____
R	_____	L	_____
W	_____	G	_____
D	_____	P	_____
K	_____	U	_____
B	_____	J	_____
V	_____	A	_____

34

C: What 'C' is the substance left when a mineral has been burnt?

E: What 'E' is the most densely populated part of Britain?

I: What 'I' is beginning?

N: What 'N' was the mythical drink which conferred immortality?

R: What 'R' comes before head, wing and skin?

W: What 'W' is spoken by natives of Snowdonia?

D: What 'D' is an antelope the size of a hare?

K: What 'K' succeeded Joseph Stalin?

B: What 'B' was an early word for cinema?

V: What 'V' was paradise in Norse mythology?

F: What 'F' is a barrier – and a receiver of stolen goods?

T: What 'T' wrote poetry for more than sixty years?

S: What 'S' is an oil-rich desert kingdom?

Y: What 'Y' is a fox-hunter's cry or halloo?

L: What 'L' is apathetic or drooping?

G: What 'G' helped win India's independence?

P: What 'P' is a unit of mass, an animal enclosure – and a US poet?

U: What 'U' means the month proceeding this one?

J: What 'J' is the ancient Samurai combat form using throws?

A: What 'A' was taught by Plato – and himself taught Alexander the Great?

F	____	N ____
O	____	J ____
K	____	S ____
R	____	H ____
T	____	U ____
A	____	G ____
E	____	M ____
B	____	W ____
P	____	C ____
D	____	L ____

35

F: What 'F' is an enthusiastic supporter – and a device for circulating air?

O: What 'O' is the capital of Canada?

K: What 'K' was the first Mongul Emperor of China?

R: What 'R' is any savage-tempered animal?

T: What 'T' is a unit of measure of gas?

A: What 'A' mechanised cotton spinning?

E: What 'E' is a rich green variety of beryl?

B: What 'B' is the science of life?

P: What 'P' is a small sea-snail living on the shore?

D: What 'D' means to discourage, intimidate – and press herrings down in a barrel?

N: What 'N' is laughing gas?

J: What 'J' invaded England in the fifth century?

S: What 'S' is an autonomous Mediterranean island?

H: What 'H' is the antonym to Heaven?

U: What 'U' is higher?

G: What 'G' is a spirit, a trap – and a machine for seeding cotton?

M: What 'M' was fascist dictator of Italy?

W: What 'W' comes before band, watch, and drop?

C: What 'C' is a large ruminant able to go for long periods without water?

L: What 'L' is an old nautical term for port (or left)?

M _____   L _____

O _____   S _____

K _____   T _____

D _____   R _____

J _____   C _____

P _____   E _____

H _____   A _____

W _____   V _____

F _____   G _____

B _____   N _____

36

M: What 'M' is a small, half-wild horse?

O: What 'O' is a square-based column with a pyramidal top?

K: What 'K' was Kenya's first president?

D: What 'D' is soft, drab coral shaped like a human hand?

J: What 'J' is a preserve made from fruit?

P: What 'P' was an English satiric poet?

H: What 'H' is another name for bumble-bee?

W: What 'W' is a perennial plant – and a girl not asked to dance?

F: What 'F' is cat-like?

B: What 'B' is a type of paper, a restraint and a secret agent?

L: What 'L' is a metallic element, symbol Pb?

S: What 'S' is to sound like something being pulled out of mud?

T: What 'T' is the second largest US state?

R: What 'R' was a French sculptor?

C: What 'C''s teachings are the basis of Scottish presbyterianism?

E: What 'E' preserves dead bodies from decay?

A: What 'A' was the sacred chest of the Hebrews?

V: What 'V' is the brightest of the planets?

G: What 'G' composed the folk-opera *Porgy and Bess*?

N: What 'N' was the Greek goddess of victory?

C _____   B _____

I _____   Q _____

N _____   H _____

O _____   L _____

F _____   S _____

K _____   R _____

A _____   E _____

P _____   M _____

D _____   T _____

J _____   U _____

37

C: What 'C' is the silvery-white metallic element, symbol Ca?

I: What 'I' were conquered by the Spanish in Peru?

N: What 'N' is bounded by the North Sea, Belgium and West Germany?

O: What 'O' is the most intelligent invertebrate?

F: What 'F' discovered penicillin?

K: What 'K' is German for children's garden?

A: What 'A' is a large-mouthed fish of the Herring family?

P: What 'P' was destroyed by the volcano Vesuvius?

D: What 'D' comes before clean, rot and ice?

J: What 'J' is an agitated bath?

B: What 'B' is the prayer-book of the Catholic clergy?

Q: What 'Q' is a small edible game bird?

H: What 'H' is the Caribbean island south-east of Cuba?

L: What 'L' is transparent material cut so at least one surface is rounded?

S: What 'S' is a planet with at least fifteen satellites?

R: What 'R' is the South American 'ostrich'?

E: What 'E' is a vestment worn by a Jewish high priest?

M: What 'M' is an edible plant with bright yellow flowers?

T: What 'T' is the capital of Japan?

U: What 'U' is a marriage, a workers' association – and a combination of parts?

G _____   I _____

Y _____   L _____

A _____   P _____

T _____   O _____

V _____   H _____

S _____   F _____

U _____   D _____

B _____   M _____

E _____   J _____

N _____   R _____

38

G: What 'G' was a French artist who painted in the South Pacific?

Y: What 'Y' is a devotee of yoga – and a bear?

A: What 'A' is a deciduous tree of the genus *Fraxinus*?

T: What 'T' comes before graph, kinesis and scope?

V: What 'V' were Odin's handmaidens?

S: What 'S' is a landlocked country with three official languages?

U: What 'U' is going alternatively up and down?

B: What 'B' is a female wolf?

E: What 'E' is when the sun is directly overhead at the equator?

N: What 'N' is England's horse-racing capital?

I: What 'I' controls the supply of sugar from the blood to the muscles?

L: What 'L' was a 17th century philosopher?

P: What 'P' was introduced to Britain from Asia – for sport?

O: What 'O' are quartz-like forms of hydrous silica, prized as gems?

H: What 'H' could get out of anything?

F: What 'F' is complete and ignominious failure?

D: What 'D' is a spotted cube, a plinth and an engraved stamp for coining?

M: What 'M' is a slug or snail?

J: What 'J' is named after a Roman two-faced god?

R: What 'R' is a mass for the dead?

C _____	F _____
E _____	T _____
I _____	S _____
N _____	Y _____
R _____	L _____
W _____	G _____
D _____	P _____
K _____	U _____
B _____	J _____
V _____	A _____

39

C: What 'C' was a Nobel Prize-winning French novelist?

E: What 'E' is a young eel?

I: What 'I' are electrically-charged atoms?

N: What 'N' is a Central American republic?

R: What 'R' is a honey badger?

W: What 'W' is a term used for stopping a horse?

D: What 'D' is unusually small?

K: What 'K' succeeded Nikita Khrushchev?

B: What 'B' is the upper nose, a card game, and a road-bearing structure?

V: What 'V' is the world's smallest state?

F: What 'F' means fruitful or fertile?

T: What 'T' carries sleeping sickness?

S: What 'S' is a ruler's mistress – and a seedless raisin?

Y: What 'Y' is affirmative?

L: What 'L' is the insect order including butterflies and moths?

G: What 'G' wrote *The Forsythe Saga*?

P: What 'P' was a 19th century French art movement?

U: What 'U' is a large overcoat – and a part of Ireland?

J: What 'J' is a fragrant climber of the olive family?

A: What 'A' is a long-eared quadruped with a tufted tail?

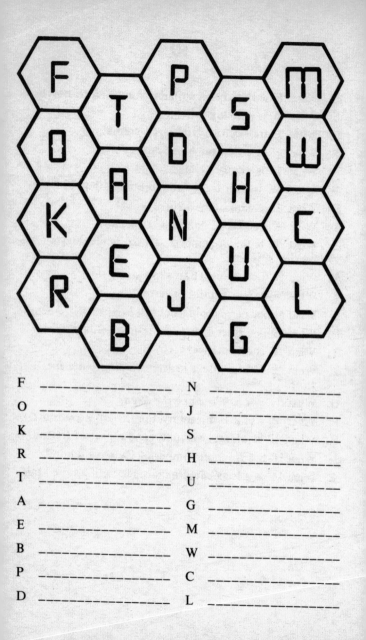

F _____   N _____

O _____   J _____

K _____   S _____

R _____   H _____

T _____   U _____

A _____   G _____

E _____   M _____

B _____   W _____

P _____   C _____

D _____   L _____

40

F: What 'F' led the Labour Party from 1980 to 1983?

O: What 'O' is the largest living bird?

K: What 'K' invented 'shuttle service' diplomacy?

R: What 'R' can all carry plague?

T: What 'T' lies between Algeria and Libya?

A: What 'A' is Hebrew for 'so be it'?

E: What 'E' is a measure in typography?

B: What 'B' has the human skeleton 206 of?

P: What 'P' is an instrument of torture – for squeezing fingers?

D: What 'D' was invented by the founder of the Nobel Prize?

N: What 'N' is December 25th?

J: What 'J' is a sailing ship, rubbish – and slang for drugs?

S: What 'S' was an Irish vegetarian playwright?

H: What 'H' lies between Guatemala and Nicaragua?

U: What 'U' do you take when you're offended?

G: What 'G' is a legendary grave-robber that feeds on corpses?

M: What 'M' is a gun, a cement mixture and a hard vessel?

W: What 'W' is an odour or puff of air?

C: What 'C' is an engraving in relief on a stone?

L: What 'L' was a Renaissance genius?

M _ _ _ _ _ _ _ _ _ _ _ _ _ _ _ _   L _ _ _ _ _ _ _ _ _ _ _ _ _ _ _

O _ _ _ _ _ _ _ _ _ _ _ _ _ _ _ _   L _ _ _ _ _ _ _ _ _ _ _ _ _ _ _

K _ _ _ _ _ _ _ _ _ _ _ _ _ _ _ _   T _ _ _ _ _ _ _ _ _ _ _ _ _ _ _

D _ _ _ _ _ _ _ _ _ _ _ _ _ _ _ _   R _ _ _ _ _ _ _ _ _ _ _ _ _ _ _

J _ _ _ _ _ _ _ _ _ _ _ _ _ _ _ _   C _ _ _ _ _ _ _ _ _ _ _ _ _ _ _

P _ _ _ _ _ _ _ _ _ _ _ _ _ _ _ _   E _ _ _ _ _ _ _ _ _ _ _ _ _ _ _

H _ _ _ _ _ _ _ _ _ _ _ _ _ _ _ _   A _ _ _ _ _ _ _ _ _ _ _ _ _ _ _

W _ _ _ _ _ _ _ _ _ _ _ _ _ _ _ _   V _ _ _ _ _ _ _ _ _ _ _ _ _ _ _

F _ _ _ _ _ _ _ _ _ _ _ _ _ _ _ _   G _ _ _ _ _ _ _ _ _ _ _ _ _ _ _

B _ _ _ _ _ _ _ _ _ _ _ _ _ _ _ _   N _ _ _ _ _ _ _ _ _ _ _ _ _ _ _

41

M: What 'M' is the fine white hair of Angora goats?

O: What 'O' is the West?

K: What 'K' comes before start, back and off?

D: What 'D' are forever?

J: What 'J' is the largest of the Channel Islands?

P: What 'P' is a voracious South American fish?

H: What 'H' is a four inch measure used in reckoning the height of horses?

W: What 'W' is a squiggle?

F: What 'F' founded the largest monastic order in the Catholic church?

B: What 'B' is an Australian bird that paints its nest?

L: What 'L' comes from wool and is a base for ointments?

S: What 'S' was the English poet who drowned in Italy?

T: What 'T' is the longest road bridge in Britain?

R: What 'R' is a highly ornamental style of art?

C: What 'C' is a watercourse with locks?

E: What 'E' are a mongoloid people with yellow skin and black hair?

A: What 'A' is the capital of South Australia?

V: What 'V' is a fabric with a soft, dense pile?

G: What 'G' scored over 54,000 runs in first-class cricket?

N: What 'N' is a neutral particle which carries energy and spin?

C _____
I _____
N _____
O _____
F _____
K _____
A _____
P _____
D _____
J _____

B _____
Q _____
H _____
L _____
S _____
R _____
E _____
M _____
T _____
U _____

42

C: What 'C' are the thirteen volcanic islands off north-west Africa?

I: What 'I' is the tendency of all bodies to resist changes in motion?

N: What 'N' 'sang in Berkeley Square'?

O: What 'O' are birds that largely live on grazing animals?

F: What 'F' was the American statesman who invented the lightning conductor?

K: What 'K' is a low island in the Caribbean?

A: What 'A' is the only armoured mammal?

P: What 'P' comes before nut, sty and tail?

D: What 'D' is a roof shaped like an inverted bowl?

J: What 'J' is a semite?

B: What 'B' is an underarm swelling – and is a type of plague?

Q: What 'Q' is an excavation – and object of pursuit?

H: What 'H' is a TV quizmaster?

L: What 'L' stands for light amplifications by stimulated emission of radiation?

S: What 'S' is tropical grassland?

R: What 'R' is a public performance of cowboy skills?

E: What 'E' is a saracen prince or governor?

M: What 'M' are members of the church of 'Jesus Christ of Latter-day Saints'?

T: What 'T' is a display of childish bad temper?

U: What 'U' means having no like?

G _____	I _____
Y _____	L _____
A _____	P _____
T _____	O _____
V _____	H _____
S _____	F _____
U _____	D _____
B _____	M _____
E _____	J _____
N _____	R _____

43

G: What 'G' is the useless rock in which ore is found?

Y: What 'Y' is volunteer cavalry recruited from farmers?

A: What 'A' was the first man on the moon?

T: What 'T' is someone who never drinks alcohol?

V: What 'V' were raiders and pirates?

S: What 'S' comes before flower, stroke and glasses?

U: What 'U' is a moslem doctor of theology?

B: What 'B' is the world's third largest island?

E: What 'E' is the obstruction of an artery?

N: What 'N' is an inert gas minutely present in air?

I: What 'I' are tusks?

L: What 'L' was half a comedy team – and a tree?

P: What 'P' was a woman's saddle put behind a man's on a horse?

O: What 'O' grow gems?

H: What 'H' ruled Austria for over 600 years?

F: What 'F' is the largest river of Papua, New Guinea – and is an insect?

D: What 'D' are sold as 'rock salmon'?

M: What 'M' was the only impressionist painter fully recognised in his lifetime?

J: What 'J' is a throwing spear?

R: What 'R' are snakes with a warning signal?

Puzzle grid (hexagons):

C R B S P
E V U
W Y
I F J
D L A
N T G
K

C	_____	
E	_____	
I	_____	
N	_____	
R	_____	
W	_____	
D	_____	
K	_____	
B	_____	
V	_____	

F	_____	
F	_____	
T	_____	
S	_____	
Y	_____	
L	_____	
G	_____	
P	_____	
U	_____	
J	_____	
A	_____	

44

C: What 'C' eat meat?

E: What 'E' is the funnel-shaped mouth of a river?

I: What 'I' is a major religion?

N: What 'N' might be called 'the pits'?

R: What 'R' comes before worthy, hog and side?

W: What 'W' is a tepee?

D: What 'D' is a lure or enticement for ducks?

K: What 'K' was a short-lived English poet?

B: What 'B' comes back?

V: What 'V' is a vegetarian who avoids all animal derivatives?

F: What 'F' is Western Australia's principal port?

T: What 'T' was a melodious Russian composer?

S: What 'S' means: make dizzy?

Y: What 'Y' is used in breadmaking?

L: What 'L' is the main food-producing part of a plant?

G: What 'G' are flies with only one pair of wings?

P: What 'P' was the pupil of Socrates and teacher of Aristotle?

U: What 'U' is another word for Hindustani?

J: What 'J' are lily-trotters?

A: What 'A' is a social hymenopterous insect?

F _____   N _____

O _____   J _____

K _____   S _____

R _____   H _____

T _____   U _____

A _____   G _____

E _____   M _____

B _____   W _____

P _____   C _____

D _____   L _____

45

F: What 'F' is a litter of pigs?

O: What 'O' means not transmitting light?

K: What 'K' wrote *If*?

R: What 'R' is a type of deer – and a mass of eggs?

T: What 'T' is the longest river in England?

A: What 'A' was the first Roman emperor?

E: What 'E' is a demand for more?

B: What 'B' are snakes that suffocate their prey?

P: What 'P' is a flute with an octave higher range than normal flutes?

D: What 'D' is government by two independent authorities?

N: What 'N' is an ice-cream – and a native of Naples?

J: What 'J' is a randomly mingled mass of things?

S: What 'S' built the first locomotive for a public railway?

H: What 'H' is one of the largest flat fishes?

U: What 'U' is impossibly ideal?

G: What 'G' were the secret police of Nazi Germany?

M: What 'M' is the tower of a mosque?

W: What 'W' comes before netting, wool and worm?

C: What 'C' lost his head in 1649?

L: What 'L' is a white blood cell?

M _____ L _____

O _____ S _____

K _____ T _____

D _____ R _____

J _____ C _____

P _____ E _____

H _____ A _____

W _____ V _____

F _____ G _____

B _____ N _____

46

M: What 'M' is the principal alkaloid of opium?

O: What 'O' are nocturnal birds of prey?

K: What 'K' was the USA's first Catholic president?

D: What 'D' is a chair, a pack of cards and a ship's floor?

J: What 'J' is a woman of stately beauty?

P: What 'P' was an impressionist landscape painter?

H: What 'H' is the growing of plants without soil?

W: What 'W' is a marvel?

F: What 'F' is the second month of the Gregorian calendar?

B: What 'B' is the capital of Queensland?

L: What 'L' coined the word 'oxygen'?

S: What 'S' means under the skin?

T: What 'T' is the soft white element found in the ore cassiterite?

R: What 'R' is a rude sound – and a red fruit?

C: What 'C' was the 18th century Swede who gave his name to a temperature scale?

E: What 'E' is an unwritten code of behaviour?

A: What 'A' is the largest city in New Zealand?

V: What 'V' is a tropical climbing orchid?

G: What 'G' is a graceful African antelope?

N: What 'N' is the lowest high tide?

C _____	B _____
I _____	Q _____
N _____	H _____
O _____	L _____
F _____	S _____
K _____	R _____
A _____	E _____
P _____	M _____
D _____	T _____
J _____	U _____

47

C: What 'C' is a church dignitary – and a shot in billiards?

I: What 'I' means to 'accuse by legal process'?

N: What 'N' comes before lace, tie and line?

O: What 'O' is a portent?

F: What 'F' are flowerless, seedless plants that reproduce by scattering spores?

K: What 'K' is the second book of Islam?

A: What 'A' wrote *Pride and Prejudice*?

P: What 'P' is a republic in south-western Europe?

D: What 'D' are probably the most intelligent mammals after man?

J: What 'J' is eleven times the diameter of Earth?

B: What 'B' means cloyed or tired of pleasure?

Q: What 'Q' is an entertaining test of knowledge?

H: What 'H' was a German composer who lived in England?

L: What 'L' is forty days of fasting?

S: What 'S' shoot their mates with a 'love dart'?

R: What 'R' is a flat fish and a beam of light?

E: What 'E' do the Australians call 'gum tree'?

M: What 'M' followed the Ming dynasty in China?

T: What 'T' occupies a high, windswept plateau of south-central Asia?

U: What 'U' means to chide or reproach?

G _____ I _____

Y _____ L _____

A _____ P _____

T _____ O _____

V _____ H _____

S _____ F _____

U _____ D _____

B _____ M _____

E _____ J _____

N _____ R _____

48

G: What 'G' is a slum area where a minority group lives?

Y: What 'Y' was William Pitt known as?

A: What 'A' was the first archbishop of Canterbury?

T: What 'T' is the Malay word for lord or master?

V: What 'V' is to disappear?

S: What 'S' is to walk heavily, baffle – and dismiss a cricketer?

U: What 'U' do the Australians call an apartment?

B: What 'B' is a metalloid element, symbol B?

E: What 'E' means short-lived?

N: What 'N' is a structure where animals live?

I: What 'I' was the birthplace of civilisation?

L: What 'L' successfully defended his world heavyweight title twenty-six times?

P: What 'P' is best known for its pungent pong?

O: What 'O' comes after carry, catch and hold?

H: What 'H' won the Nobel Prize for literature in 1954?

F: What 'F' is a hispanic festival?

D: What 'D' is Old and New – and the capital of India?

M: What 'M' is uncrystalised sugar cane juice after boiling?

J: What 'J' is to run at a slow trot?

R: What 'R' measures earthquakes?

C _____

E _____

I _____

N _____

R _____

W _____

D _____

K _____

B _____

V _____

F _____

T _____

S _____

Y _____

L _____

G _____

P _____

U _____

J _____

A _____

49

C: What 'C' is an American reindeer?

E: What 'E' is a sharp-pointed duelling sword?

I: What 'I' is an animal with no backbone?

N: What 'N' is the doctrine that rejects all doctrine?

R: What 'R' is an international news agency?

W: What 'W' is a cuddly-looking Australian marsupial?

D: What 'D' is where President Kennedy was shot?

K: What 'K' was a 16th century Scottish reformer?

B: What 'B' is a two masted, square-rigged vessel?

V: What 'V' is wilful defacement of property?

F: What 'F' is an intricate manipulation, a swindle – and a violin?

T: What 'T' was the hanging place where Marble Arch now stands?

S: What 'S' composed over 400 waltzes?

Y: What 'Y' is wool oil – and the yellow of an egg?

L: What 'L' is a dictionary?

G: What 'G' is a computerised system of money transfer?

P: What 'P' is a large, spiny rodent?

U: What 'U' is a fruit somewhere between grapefruit and tangerine?

J: What 'J' contains some two-thirds of the population of Indonesia?

A: What 'A' is the world's second largest continent?

F
T
P
M
O
D
S
A
H
W
K
N
C
E
U
R
J
L
B
G

F _____   N _____
O _____   J _____
K _____   S _____
R _____   H _____
T _____   U _____
A _____   G _____
E _____   M _____
B _____   W _____
P _____   C _____
D _____   L _____

50

F: What 'F' is the acid secreted by ants?

O: What 'O' means to decide in favour of something?

K: What 'K' is the most rapidly growing industrial country in the world?

R: What 'R' is a grain-yielding grass?

T: What 'T' is three persons in one God?

A: What 'A' is a branch of the Mediterranean between Greece and Turkey?

E: What 'E' comes before librium, distant and lateral?

B: What 'B' is salt water?

P: What 'P' inhabited Scotland in pre-Roman times?

D: What 'D' are extinct Mesozoic reptiles?

N: What 'N' is a wanderer?

J: What 'J' is a fishing line – and a lively dance?

S: What 'S' was a major French novelist whose works include *Le Rouge et Le Noir*?

H: What 'H' is the religion of most Indians?

U: What 'U' is a roguish youngster?

G: What 'G' is radiation used to fight cancer?

M: What 'M' calls the Islamic faithful to prayer?

W: What 'W' is the ridge between horses' shoulder blades?

C: What 'C' is a knitted jumper with buttons or a zip down the front?

L: What 'L' is the literary text of an opera?

M _____   L _____

O _____   S _____

K _____   T _____

D _____   R _____

J _____   C _____

P _____   E _____

H _____   A _____

W _____   V _____

F _____   G _____

B _____   N _____

51

M: What 'M' is the material used to slow neutrons in an atomic pile?

O: What 'O' does the dove of peace carry?

K: What 'K' was the 18th century German philosopher?

D: What 'D' is a ten-footed crustacean?

J: What 'J' is related to the crow?

P: What 'P' is a very fine type of pottery?

H: What 'H' means cornucopia?

W: What 'W' is a limbless invertebrate?

F: What 'F' is wood or metal fastened alongside something to strengthen it?

B: What 'B' is the capital of South America's largest country?

L: What 'L' comes before boat, guard and line?

S: What 'S' ruled Russia for almost thirty years?

T: What 'T' means curt or concise?

R: What 'R' is a linked chain of prayer beads?

C: What 'C' is a small craft pointed at both ends?

E: What 'E' was the manifestation of Christ to the Magi?

A: What 'A' did Alexander the Great found in 332 BC?

V: What 'V' is an endorsement on a passport?

G: What 'G' is the world's tallest animal?

N: What 'N' is a loop – that rhymes with a US deer?

C _____
I _____
N _____
O _____
F _____
K _____
A _____
P _____
D _____
J _____

B _____
Q _____
H _____
L _____
S _____
R _____
E _____
M _____
T _____
U _____

52

C: What 'C' is a measure of weight for precious stones?

I: What 'I' is the world's second most populated country?

N: What 'N' is architecture characterised by semi-circular arches?

O: What 'O' is a pungent white bulb used in cooking?

F: What 'F' comes before bug, guard and side?

K: What 'K' is the largest living lizard?

A: What 'A' is the capital of Ethiopia?

P: What 'P' is an inflammation of the lungs?

D: What 'D' is a kind of small pigeon?

J: What 'J' is a very large truck?

B: What 'B' was a race found by the Romans in England?

Q: What 'Q' is a witty or sarcastic observation?

H: What 'H' was a blind epic poet?

L: What 'L' was abolished in 1964 as a scientific unit of volume?

S: What 'S' is an odd-looking African cat?

R: What 'R' is a gambling game that highly favours the casino?

E: What 'E' is the outer layer of our skin?

M: What 'M' is a strong scented plant – and a place that makes money?

T: What 'T' is also called 'lock-jaw'?

U: What 'U' are Russian mountains?

G _____ I _____

Y _____ L _____

A _____ P _____

T _____ O _____

V _____ H _____

S _____ F _____

U _____ D _____

B _____ M _____

E _____ J _____

N _____ R _____

53

G: What 'G' is a wildebeest?

Y: What 'Y' is the Hindu god who judges the dead?

A: What 'A' are the highest mountains in Europe?

T: What 'T' means having made a valid will?

V: What 'V' is a person of great prestige?

S: What 'S' spends some 75% of its life asleep?

U: What 'U' did the *Voyager* space-probe photograph?

B: What 'B' is a nearly spherical underground stem?

E: What 'E' contains 20% of the world's population?

N: What 'N' means marriageable?

I: What 'I' is a climbing evergreen plant with shiny leaves?

L: What 'L' is to lean to one side?

P: What 'P' is a radioactive metallic element?

O: What 'O' is a red-brown ape?

H: What 'H' is converted from sucrose to mixed fructose and glucose?

F: What 'F' is the Moslem sabbath?

D: What 'D' is an aboriginal wind instrument?

M: What 'M' had the golden touch?

J: What 'J' controls an aircraft's elevators and ailerons?

R: What 'R' is a spirit made from molasses?

C _____	F _____
E _____	T _____
I _____	S _____
N _____	Y _____
R _____	L _____
W _____	G _____
D _____	P _____
K _____	U _____
B _____	J _____
V _____	A _____

54

C: What 'C' is an exaggerated drawing of someone?

E: What 'E' is a republic that is 96% desert?

I: What 'I' means 'to put in an urn'?

N: What 'N' is the explosion of a star?

R: What 'R' suck up to sharks?

W: What 'W' is a kind of North American marmot?

D: What 'D' is the chief material of the chromosomes found in every living cell?

K: What 'K' activates Qantas?

B: What 'B' is the central, most complex part of the nervous system?

V: What 'V' is a loud, overbearing woman?

F: What 'F' are plants that reproduce from spores and lack chlorophyll?

T: What 'T' is a mineral valued as a gem?

S: What 'S' is the world's second smallest mammal?

Y: What 'Y' is a South American water opossum?

L: What 'L' is a stretcher, rubbish – and an animal's offspring?

G: What 'G' is to grind the teeth?

P: What 'P' is second to last?

U: What 'U' means suave and courteous?

J: What 'J' is an alcoholic mint drink?

A: What 'A' is an eye defect where the lens cannot focus properly?

F _____	N _____
O _____	J _____
K _____	S _____
R _____	H _____
T _____	U _____
A _____	G _____
E _____	M _____
B _____	W _____
P _____	C _____
D _____	L _____

55

F: What 'F' is a nine-gallon wooden cask?

O: What 'O' is a Scandinavian unit of currency?

K: What 'K' means 'of motion'?

R: What 'R' are textiles containing cellulose?

T: What 'T' is a devastating wind?

A: What 'A' is the snake that killed Cleopatra?

E: What 'E' is an attempt or a composition?

B: What 'B' is a system whereby the blind can read?

P: What 'P' are the main chemical substances of living matter?

D: What 'D' is a disease that blocks the breathing passages?

N: What 'N' is bare?

J: What 'J' is a special anniversary?

S: What 'S' is the wind instrument invented by Adolphe Sax?

H: What 'H' is a short-tailed largely nocturnal rodent?

U: What 'U' is pressing?

G: What 'G' is a stick, lump – or mouth?

M: What 'M' painted a 6,000 square-foot masterpiece?

W: What 'W' is done at the Wall in Jerusalem?

C: What 'C' has the head of a man and body of a horse?

L: What 'L' are a type of voracious grasshopper?

Solution: Puzzle 1

M: Man; O: Oedipus; K; Kebab; D: Dalmatian; J: Japan; P: Piggott;
H: Hick; W: Wallaby; F: Freud; B: Bridgetown; L: Lacrosse; S: Swan;
T: Taylor; R: Rabbit; C: Cairn; E: Eager; A: Air; V: Vesuvius; G: Gagarin;
N: Nicotine.

Solution: Puzzle 2

C: Cue; I: Ibsen; N: NAAFI; O: Othello; F: Femur; K: Kampuchea;
A: Aluminium; P: Piquet (Nelson); D: Damascus; J: Jihad; B: Baboon;
Q: Quick; H: Help!; L: Lawrence, (T.E.); S: Saccharin; R: Raccoon; E: Ease;
M: Madeira; T: Tarzan; U: UFO.

Solution: Puzzle 3

G: Gila monster; Y: Yearling; A: America; T: Thatcher; V: Vole;
S: Sahara; U: Umbrella; B: Badger; E: Earth; N: Nabob; I: Ice; L: Landseer;
P: Papyrus; O: Oak apple; H: Houri; F: Faucet; D: Dachau; M: Macaw;
J: Jodhpur(s); R: Radio.

Solution: Puzzle 4

C: Cult; E: Einstein; I: Ireland; N: Nap; R: Rabbi; W: Walloon;
D: Daddy-long-legs; K: Kaput; B: Bath; V: Victoria; F: Fahrenheit;
T: Teddy; S: Salamander; Y: Yearn; L: Lamprey; G: Gallup (poll);
P: Panther; U: Ultramarine; J: Joint; A: Amethyst.

Solution: Puzzle 5

F: Filly; O: Olivier; K: Kangaroo; R: Race; T: Tipperary; A: Anaconda;
E: Elizabeth; B: Bacchus; P: Pagan; D: Dali; N: Nightingale (Florence);
J: Joist; S: Sage; H: Host; U: Uganda; G: Gavial; M: Macao; W: Water;
C: Cactus; L: Lady.

Solution: Puzzle 6

M: Mackenzie; O: Ohm; K: Kestrel; D: Daguerreotype; J: Joyce (James);
P: Pluto; H: Hepplewhite; W: Wampum; F: Files; B: Bad; L: Laager;
S: Saigon; T: Tabernacle; R: Rabat; C: Cadmium; E: Edward VIII;
A: Amoeba; V: Voodoo; G: Gecko; N: Narwhal.

Solution: Puzzle 7

C: Calorie; I: Ivan (the Terrible); N: Newts; O: Oakum; F: Face;
K: Kinkajou; A: Amsterdam; P: Pearl; D: Descartes; J: Jeep; B: Baden-
Powell; Q: Queue; H: Hay; L: Labile; S: Salmon; R: Ramsey; E: Everest;
M: Mafia; T: Taiwan; U: Ulysses.

Solution: Puzzle 8

G: Gander; Y: Yard; A: Amino; T: Taipei; V: Vampire; S: Salt; U: Uudset;
B: Beetle; E: Equador; N: Nibs; I: Ibis; L: La Paz; P: Pectin; O: Obeah;
H: Hadrian; F: Fallow; D: Dab; M: Madrid; J: James I; R: Rabid.

Solution: Puzzle 9

C: Canada; E: Evaporation; I: Insects; N: Nexus; R: Rangoon; W: Wankel;
D: Duplex; K: Keen; B: Bach, (J. S.); V: Volt; F: Falcon; T: Turnbull
(Wendy); S: Sand dollar; Y: Youth; L: Lac; G: Garret; P: Patrick (St);
U: Ulcer; J: Jerry; A: Angola.

Solution: Puzzle 10

F: Factotum; O: Obfuscate; K: Kapok; R: Radish; T: Taboo; A: Antibody;
E: Equator; B: Bacon; P: Palolo; D: Dado; N: Niggard; J: Jet;
S: Sacrament; H: Hallowe'en; U: Uruguay; G: Galago; M: Machiavelli;
W: Wan; C: Calcutta; L: Ladybird.

Solution: Puzzle 11

M: Macaroni; O: Ocelot; K: Keg; D: Daltonism; J: Jehovah; P: Pelé;
H: Hence; W: Waist; F: Fairy; B: Battery; L: Labrador; S: Saladin;
T: Thomas; R: Radar; C: Cambrian; E: ERNIE (Electronic Random
Number Indicator Equipment); A: Aden; V: Valentine; G: Gang;
N: Natterjack.

Solution: Puzzle 12

C: Cull; I: Iliad; N: Nile; O: Obi; F: Friar; K: Karma; A: Ape; P: Pin;
D: Dam; J: Jackal; B: Badger; Q: Quack; H: Hitler; L: Leningrad;
S: Samurai; R: Rain; E: Elgar; M: Mackerel; T: Theta; U: Ukulele.

Solution: Puzzle 13

G: Garotte; Y: Yelp; A: Adagio; T: Tendon; V: Velázquez; S: Sargasso (Sea); U: USA; B: Bedlam; E: Eddy (Mary Baker); N: Nairobi; I: Ill; L: Lava; P: Pisces; O: Oblate; H: Hashish; F: Ferret; D: Diogenes; M: Mary (Queen of Scots); J: Jade; R: Rome.

Solution: Puzzle 14

C: Calligraphy; E: Eisenhower; I: Isis; N: Neanderthal; R: Red; W: White (Jimmy); D: Date Line; K: Kaolin; B: Balzac; V: Vacuum; F: Family; T: Tarantella; S: San Francisco; Y: Yen; L: Libreville; G: Garlic; P: Petrarch; U: University; J: Jaguar; A: Anthem.

Solution: Puzzle 15

F: Farewell Cape; O: Oboe; K: Kilt; R: Roosevelt; T: Thomson's; A: Arch; E: Euripides; B: Bangkok; P: Picasso; D: Dank; N: Nero; J: Jack; S: Sandpipers; H: Hydro; U: Unicorn; G: Ganges; M: Mamba; W: Wagner; C: Cuff; L: Libya.

Solution: Puzzle 16

M: Mozart; O: Oblong; K: Karachi; D: Donne; J: Jaundice; P: Panther; H: Hulk; W: Weather; F: Faroes; B: Backgammon; L: Lima; S: Sardine; T: Tabasco; R: Rhodesia; C: Crypt; E: Eiffel; A: Appendix; V: Verne; G: Garnet; N: Nebula.

Solution: Puzzle 17

C: Cuddy; I: I-Ching; N: Nasser; O: Occiput; F: Factor; K: Kalahari; A: Abacus; P: Pigeon; D: Dostoevsky; J: Johannesburg; B: Bellow; Q: Quinine; H: Hornet; L: Lisbon; S: Sanskrit; R: Reagan; E: Eel; M: Magazine; T: Table; U: Ulna.

Solution: Puzzle 18

G: Gas; Y: Yellow; A: Apartheid; T: Terrapin; V: Voltaire; S: Slipper; U: Uranium; B: Bangladesh; E: Elegy; N: Nectarine; I: Impala; L: Lactose; P: Pineapple; O: Obliged; H: Hydrogen; F: Fag; D: Dead; M: Mallee Fowl; J: Josephine; R: Rocky.

Solution: Puzzle 19

C: Crumb; E: Ethiopia; I: Ireland; N: Nark; R: Rubik; W: Warthog; D: Dearth; K: Khartoum; B: Baseball; V: Vacillate; F: Fairy; T: Tack; S: Scarab; Y: Yiddish; L: Limpopo; G: Glasgow; P: Pong; U: Umber; J: Johnson; A: Aerosol.

Solution: Puzzle 20

F: Fez; O: Oil; K: Ku Klux Klan; R: Reykjavik; T: Taffeta; A: Alder; E: Elephant; B: Beelzebub (or Belial); P: Pillar; D: Danube; N: Nehru; J: Jugular; S: Shilling; H: Husbandry; U: USSR; G: Grittar; M: Manatee; W: Walton; C: Choir; L: Lizard.

Solution: Puzzle 21

M: Mole; O: Off; K: Kingston; D: Dryden; J: Jargon; P: Porpoise; H: Hannibal; W: Wicket; F: Fiji; B: Becket (Thomas); L: Leech; S: Scorpions; T: Taffy; R: Rembrandt; C: California; E: Egg; A: Albert; V: Vultures; G: Glass; N: Neptune.

Solution: Puzzle 22

C: Caligula; I: Imam; N: Nessie; O: Oesophagus; F: Fleas; K: Kremlin; A: Acids; P: Pyramids; D: Dunstan; J: Jar; B: Bipedal; Q: Queensland; H: Hardy; L: Larder; S: Seahorses; R: Robot; E: Ebony; M: Maple leaf; T: Termites; U: Ultra.

Solution: Puzzle 23

G: Greenwich; Y: Yak; A: Algae; T: Tiger; V: Valet; S: Sartre (Jean Paul); U: Umpteen; B: Benedictine; E: Eland; N: Nelson; I: Imbecile (or Idiot); L: Limpid; P: Pope; O: Ovid; H: Ham; F: Fable; D: Day; M: Mandrill; J: Jung; R: Runnymede.

Solution: Puzzle 24

C: Chicago; E: Edison; I: Iguana; N: Nash; R: Raft; W: Wax; D: Dandelion; K: Kiwi; B: Bauxite; V: Valance; F: Finland; T: TVP (Textured Vegetable Protein); S: Sack; Y: Yeti; L: Liszt; G: Greenland; P: Pyorrhoea; U: Understudy; J: John-Paul II; A: Alloy.

Solution: Puzzle 25

F: Fang; O: Owen; K: Knife; R: Ravel; T: Theodolite; A: Alpaca; E: Effendi;
B: Bill; P: Python; D: Dumas; N: Nicholas II; J: Jack; S: Santa Claus;
H: Hastings; U: Utter; G: Guatemala; M: Magenta; W: Wombles;
C: Cape Cod; L: Lapis Lazuli.

Solution: Puzzle 26

M: Magnum; O: Otto I; K: Kohl; D: Danegeld; J: Jerusalem; P: Pangolin;
H: Hose; W: Wheel; F: Farouk; B: Behest; L: Lapwing; S: Sampan;
T: Tariff; R: Renoir; C: Calypso; E: Effusion; A: Amber; V: Verdun;
G: Gerbil; N: Napoleon.

Solution: Puzzle 27

C: Chub; I: Imp; N: Nixon; O: Okapi; F: Fathom; K: Kittiwake;
A: Algiers; P: Pick; D: Damocles; J: Jesuit; B: Benz; Q: Quadruped;
H: Hop; L: Lindbergh; S: Sachet; R: Ruhr; E: Epstein; M: Magma;
T: Trout; U: Us.

Solution: Puzzle 28

G: Galileo; Y: Yacht; A: Almond; T: Tobacco; V: Valletta; S: Sabot;
U: Urn; B: Bedouin; E: Equal; N: Nyerere; I: Iron; L: Langouste; P: Pike;
O: Orwell (George); H: Hammer; F: Fangio; D: Date palm; M: Mingy;
J: July; R: Richard I.

Solution: Puzzle 29

C: Chiropodists; E: Elgin; I: Impeach; N: Night; R: Raleigh (Sir Walter);
W: Weeping; D: Dauphins; K: Kidney; B: Bathometer; V: Vienna;
F: Fallout; T: Tea; S: Swahili; Y: Yobbo; L: Lincoln; G: Gel; P: Paca;
U: Utensil; J: Joan of Arc; A: Aorta.

Solution: Puzzle 30

F: Faraday; O: Offenbach; K: Kilo; R: Rockets; T: Tern; A: Asthma;
E: Emu; B: Berlin; P: Pythagoras; D: Dap; N: Narghile; J: Johnson;
S: San Salvador; H: Hermes; U: Usury; G: Genes; M: Mahogany;
W: Weekly; C: Caviar; L: Luther.

Solution: Puzzle 31

M: Mammals; O: Oman; K: Kick; D: Dark; J: James; P: Pelican; H: Hispanic; W: Wife; F: Foot; B: Bible; L: Larynx; S: Safari; T: Troglodytes; R: Raphael; C: Chock; E: Eft; A: Asphalt; V: Vicksburg; G: Geisha; N: Narcissism.

Solution: Puzzle 32

C: Cholera; I: Inane; N: Ney; O: Oporto; F: Fry (Charles B); K: Knob; A: Albino; P: Pilot; D: Deem; J: Jordan; B: Billiards; Q: Quarks; H: Hustle; L: Longfellow; S: Suez Canal; R: Robin; E: Electrode; M: Maggot; T: Tape; U: Umbilical.

Solution: Puzzle 33

G: Gainsborough; Y: Yonder; A: Anti; T: Tarragon; V: Valediction; S: Santiago; U: Undertow; B: Biretta; E: Elastic; N: Nagasaki; I: Icon; L: Lance; P: Pushkin; O: Orange; H: Hygeia; F: Falsetto; D: Darwin (Charles); M: Musk; J: Jefferson; R: Reed.

Solution: Puzzle 34

C: Calx; E: England; I: Inception (or initiation); N: Nectar; R: Red; W: Welsh; D: Dik-Dik; K: Khrushchev; B: Bioscope (or biograph); V: Valhalla; F: Fence; T: Tennyson; S: Saudi Arabia; Y: Yoicks; L: Languid; G: Gandhi; P: Pound; U: Ultimo; J: Jujitsu; A: Aristotle.

Solution: Puzzle 35

F: Fan; O: Ottawa; K: Kublai Khan; R: Rogue; T: Therm; A: Arkwright; E: Emerald; B: Biology; P: Periwinkle; D: Daunt; N: Nitrous oxide; J: Jutes; S: Sardinia; H: Hell; U: Upper; G: Gin; M: Mussolini; W: Wrist; C: Camel; L: Larboard.

Solution: Puzzle 36

M: Mustang; O: Obelisk; K: Kenyatta; D: Dead-Man's-Fingers; J: Jam; P: Pope; H: Humble-bee; W: Wallflower; F: Feline; B: Bond; L: Lead; S: Squelch; T: Texas; R: Rodin; C: Calvin; E: Embalming; A: Ark (of the Covenant); V: Venus; G: Gershwin; N: Nike.

Solution: Puzzle 37

C: Calcium; I: Incas; N: Netherlands; O: Octopus; F: Fleming;
K: Kindergarten; A: Anchovy; P: Pompeii; D: Dry; J: Jacuzzi; B: Breviary;
Q: Quail; H: Haiti; L: Lens; S: Saturn; R: Rhea; E: Ephod; M: Mustard;
T: Tokyo; U: Union.

Solution: Puzzle 38

G: Gauguin; Y: Yogi; A: Ash; T: Tele; V: Valkyries; S: Switzerland;
U: Undulation; B: Bitch; E: Equinox; N: Newmarket; I: Insulin; L: Locke;
P: Pheasant; O: Opals; H: Houdini; F: Fiasco; D: Die; M: Mollusc;
J: January; R: Requiem.

Solution: Puzzle 39

C: Camus; E: Elver; I: Ions; N: Nicaragua; R: Ratel; W: Whoa (or Wo);
D: Dwarf; K: Kosygin; B: Bridge; V: Vatican; F: Fecund; T: Tsetse (fly);
S: Sultana; Y: Yes; L: Lepidoptera; G: Galsworthy; P: Pointillism;
U: Ulster; J: Jasmine; A: Ass.

Solution: Puzzle 40

F: Foot (Michael); O: Ostrich; K: Kissinger; R: Rodents (or Rats);
T: Tunisia; A: Amen; E: Em (or En); B: Bones; P: Pilliwinks; D: Dynamite;
N: Noel (or Nativity); J: Junk; S: Shaw (George Bernard); H: Honduras;
U: Umbrage; G: Ghoul; M: Mortar; W: Whiff; C: Cameo; L: Leonardo.

Solution: Puzzle 41

M: Mohair; O: Occident; K: Kick; D: Diamonds; J: Jersey; P: Piranha;
H: Hand; W: Wiggle; F: Francis (of Assisi); B: Bower; L: Lanolin;
S: Shelley; T: Tay; R: Rococo; C: Canal; E: Eskimo; A: Adelaide;
V: Velvet; G: Grace, (W. G.); N: Neutrino.

Solution: Puzzle 42

C: Canaries; I: Inertia; N: Nightingale; O: Oxpecker; F: Franklin; K: Key;
A: Armadillo; P: Pig; D: Dome; J: Jew; B: Bubonic; Q: Quarry; H: Holness;
L: Laser; S: Savanna; R: Rodeo; E: Emir; M: Mormons; T: Tantrum;
U: Unique.

Solution: Puzzle 43

G: Gangue; Y: Yeomanry; A: Armstrong; T: Teetotal (or Temperate); V: Vikings; S: Sun; U: Ulema; B: Borneo; E: Embolism; N: Neon; I: Ivory; L: Laurel; P: Pillion; O: Oysters; H: Hapsburgs; F: Fly; D: Dogfish; M: Monet; J: Javelin; R: Rattlesnakes.

Solution: Puzzle 44

C: Carnivores; E: Estuary; I: Islam; N: Nadir; R: Road; W: Wigwam; D: Decoy; K: Keats; B: Boomerang; V: Vegan; F: Freemantle; T: Tchaikovsky; S: Stun; Y: Yeast; L: Leaf; G: Gadflies; P: Plato; U: Urdu; J: Jaçanas; A: Ant.

Solution: Puzzle 45

F: Farrow; O: Opaque; K: Kipling (Rudyard); R: Roe; T: Thames; A: Augustus; E: Encore!; B: Boa; P: Piccolo; D: Diarchy; N: Neapolitan; J: Jumble; S: Stephenson; H: Halibut; U: Utopia; G: Gestapo; M: Minaret; W: Wire; C: Charles I; L: Leucocyte.

Solution: Puzzle 46

M: Morphine; O: Owls; K: Kennedy; D: Deck; J: Junoesque; P: Pissarro; H: Hydroponics; W: Wonder; F: February; B: Brisbane; L: Lavoisier; S: Subcutaneous; T: Tin; R: Raspberry; C: Celsius; E: Etiquette; A: Auckland; V: Vanilla; G: Gazelle; N: Neap.

Solution: Puzzle 47

C: Canon; I: Indict; N: Neck; O: Omen; F: Ferns; K: Koran; A: Austen; P: Portugal; D: Dolphins; J: Jupiter; B: Blasé (or Bored); Q: Quiz; H: Handel; L: Lent; S: Snails; R: Ray; E: Eucalyptus; M: Manchu; T: Tibet; U: Upbraid.

Solution: Puzzle 48

G: Ghetto; Y: Younger; A: Augustine; T: Tuan; V: Vanish; S: Stump; U: Unit; B: Boron; E: Ephemeral; N: Nest; I: Iraq; L: Louis; P: Polecat; O: On; H: Hemingway; F: Fiesta; D: Delhi; M: Molasses; J: Jog; R: Richter (scale).

Solution: Puzzle 49

C: Caribou; E: Epée; I: Invertebrate; N: Nihilism; R: Reuter; W: Wombat;
D: Dallas; K: Knox; B: Brig; V: Vandalism; F: Fiddle; T: Tyburn;
S: Strauss; Y: Yolk; L: Lexicon; G: Giro; P: Porcupine; U: Ugli; J: Java;
A: Africa.

Solution: Puzzle 50

F: Formic; O: Opt; K: Korea, (South); R: Rice; T: Trinity; A: Aegean;
E: Equi; B: Brine; P: Picts; D: Dinosaurs; N: Nomad; J: Jig; S: Stendhal;
H: Hinduism; U: Urchin; G: Gamma; M: Muezzin; W: Withers;
C: Cardigan; L: Libretto.

Solution: Puzzle 51

M: Moderator; O: Olive (branch); K: Kant; D: Decapod; J: Jackdaw (or
Jay); P: Porcelain; H: Horn (of plenty); W: Worm; F: Fishplate; B: Brasilia;
L: Life; S: Stalin; T: Terse; R: Rosary; C: Canoe; E: Epiphany;
A: Alexandria; V: Visa; G: Giraffe; N: Noose.

Solution: Puzzle 52

C: Carat; I: India; N: Norman; O: Onion; F: Fire; K: Komodo (dragon);
A: Addis Ababa; P: Pneumonia; D: Dove; J: Juggernaut; B: Britons;
Q: Quip; H: Homer; L: Litre; S: Serval; R: Roulette; E: Epidermis;
M: Mint; T: Tetanus; U: Urals.

Solution: Puzzle 53

G: Gnu; Y: Yama; A: Alps; T: Testate; V: VIP; S: Sloth; U: Uranus;
B: Bulb; E: Europe; N: Nubile; I: Ivy; L: List; P: Plutonium;
O: Orang-utan; H: Honey; F: Friday; D: Didgeridoo; M: Midas;
J: Joystick; R: Rum.

Solution: Puzzle 54

C: Caricature; E: Egypt; I: Inurn; N: Nova; R: Remora; W: Woodchuck;
D: DNA; K: Koala; B: Brain; V: Virago; F: Fungi; T: Topaz; S: Shrew;
Y: Yapok; L: Litter; G: Gnash; P: Penultimate; U: Urbane; J: Julep;
A: Astigmatism.

Solution: Puzzle 55

F: Firkin; O: Öre; K: Kinetic; R: Rayon; T: Tornado (or Typhoon); A: Asp;
E: Essay; B: Braille; P: Proteins; D: Diphteria; N: Nude; J: Jubilee;
S: Saxophone; H: Hamster; U: Urgent; G: Gob; M: Michelangelo;
W: Wailing; C: Centaur; L: Locust.

The Freakiest, Funniest Book About Animals – _Ever!_

ODDBODS!

Bill Garnett

FIRST THERE WAS _THE NAKED APE_. THEN CAME _THE NAKED NUN_... NOW – AT LAST – THE NAKED TRUTH!

There are creatures that walk this planet which:

* _Bathe in acid_
* _Baffle Radar_
* _Turn into plants_
* _Do business – and have sex – without their heads_

You'll find them – and many others even stranger – in _ODDBODS!_

IT'S EVERYTHING YOU NEVER WANTED TO KNOW ABOUT ANIMALS – BUT WILL BE STAGGERED TO HEAR!

HUMOUR/NON-FICTION   0 7221 3809 1   £1.75

A selection of bestsellers from SPHERE

FICTION

STREET SONG	Emma Blair	£3.50 ☐
GOLDEN TRIPLE TIME	Zoe Garrison	£2.95 ☐
BEACHES	Iris Rainer Dart	£2.95 ☐
RAINBOW SOLDIERS	Walter Winward	£3.50 ☐
FAMILY ALBUM	Danielle Steel	£2.95 ☐

FILM AND TV TIE-IN

MONA LISA	John Luther Novak	£2.50 ☐
BLOCKBUSTERS GOLD RUN		£1.95 ☐
9½ WEEKS	Elizabeth McNeil	£1.95 ☐
BOON	Anthony Masters	£2.50 ☐
AUF WIEDERSEHEN PET 2	Fred Taylor	£2.75 ☐

NON-FICTION

BURTON: THE MAN BEHIND THE MYTH	Penny Junor	£2.95 ☐
THE DISAPPEARED	John Simpson & Jana Bennett	£4.95 ☐
THE LAST NAZI: THE LIFE AND TIMES OF JOSEPH MENGELE	Gerald Astor	£3.50 ☐
THE FALL OF SAIGON	David Butler	£3.95 ☐
LET'S FACE IT	Christine Piff	£2.50 ☐

All Sphere books are available at your local bookshop or newsagent, or can be ordered direct from the publisher. Just tick the titles you want and fill in the form below.

_____

Name _____

Address _____

_____

Write to Sphere Books, Cash Sales Department, P.O. Box 11, Falmouth, Cornwall TR10 9EN.

Please enclose a cheque or postal order to the value of the cover price plus:

UK: 55p for the first book, 22p for the second book and 14p for each additional book ordered to a maximum charge of £1.75.

OVERSEAS: £1.00 for the first book plus 25p per copy for each additional book.

BFPO & EIRE: 55p for the first book, 22p for the second book plus 14p per copy for the next 7 books, thereafter 8p per book.

Sphere Books reserve the right to show new retail prices on covers which may differ from those previously advertised in the text or elsewhere, and to increase postal rates in accordance with the PO.